Contents

Caught in the Web learning activities:

Acknowledgements

Written by Kelly Griffiths

The Police Community Clubs would like to thank the following for their contribution to this publication:
Published by Embrace Education Limited
Norman Kirtlan for creative ideas
Matthew Houghton for graphic design
Julie Poad for learning activities
Embrace Education Limited for sales and distribution

The Barney and Echo series

The Barney and Echo series has been developed to support parents and teachers in addressing personal, social and health education (PSHE) at key stage 1-2. The books are set in Treetop Forest and follow the adventures of Barney Eagle and Echo Squirrel.

Each title has a story relating to a PSHE subject area with activities to reinforce the learning goals. The books, which are designed to be fun and educational, can be used in a classroom setting and at home to support reading and discussion.

The series of five books also contains titles that address issues such as anti-social behaviour, internet safety and bullying. In total, the books have been distributed to more than 350,000 children across the UK.

In this title Barney has to help his friends when they start using the internet. Barney teaches his friends the importance of internet safety, not giving out personal details to strangers, internet chat rooms and the consequences of cyber bullying.

With help from Tom Stoat the Woodland Wizard, Barney helps his friends to stay safe online.

Caught in the Web

"27...28...29...30...," Echo Squirrel was counting loudly and scribbling a list into his notebook.

"31...32...33...," Echo was so busy that he didn't see his friend Barney Eagle flutter down beside him.

"Hi Echo," said Barney, stretching out his wings.
"You look very busy. What are you doing?"
Echo smiled and held up his notebook.
"I'm making a list of all my friends and I've got 33!"
"Wow," said Barney. "That's a lot."
Echo nodded excitedly, but then the smile left his face.
"It is a lot," he said. "But it's not as many as Dizzy and Spike have."

5

Barney was puzzled. After all, Echo was one of the most popular animals in Treetop Forest and 33 seemed like a lot of friends.

"They've both got computers and smart phones," Echo explained. "And now they have lots and lots of new friends who they talk to on the internet. They are so busy chatting to people online that they hardly come out to play anymore."

Barney felt sorry for Echo, when suddenly the smile returned to the squirrel's face.
"But guess what Dad is getting me tomorrow?"
Barney nodded. "I think I can guess."

Echo's smile was even wider now, lighting up his whole face. "A brand new tablet," he shouted excitedly. "I just can't wait!"

Barney was pleased for Echo but also felt quite worried about his friend.
The internet can be lots of fun, he thought to himself, but it can also be quite dangerous if you don't follow a few sensible rules.

It was time to go and as Barney flew off into the sky, he made up his mind to keep an eagle eye on Echo.

The next day after school Spike, Dizzy Rabbit and Digsby Mole were all going for tea at Echo's house and to watch Echo open his new tablet.

"Take your time," said Echo's dad.
"Be careful or you will break it before you've even opened the box!" said his mum.

Just then Barney arrived.

Echo could hardly contain his excitement. His mum and dad had bought him a tablet for doing well at school and he couldn't wait to use it. No sooner had he switched it on than the screen beamed into life and a tune played.

Spike pushed forward as the friends all crowded around the screen. "Would you like me to show you how to make new friends? There's a great new social networking site called Woodland Chat, you can talk online to animals that you have never met before and make loads of new friends."

"Before you go any further we need to have some rules to make sure that you are safe when you go online," said Echo's dad.

Echo shuffled in his chair, desperate to get started.

"First things first Echo, we need to set up a password for you."
"Why do we need to do that dad?" asked Echo.
"To keep you safe. Without a password anyone could pick up your tablet and use it," replied dad.

"But who would do that? It will only be me using the tablet," said Echo.
"People who want to pretend to be you. They could use your email, find out where you live, send messages as you and even steal from you. It's called identity theft. Will you have the tablet with you all the time, every minute of every day?" asked dad.

"Well no, not every minute," replied Echo.

"And when you take it out, can you be sure that nobody else will ever be able to use it without you knowing?"
"I Suppose not," said Echo.

Barney's **Simple Safety Rules**

Be safe and have fun

Always check with your parents before going online

Remember not to give out personal information when online

Never arrange to meet someone in person that you have only sent messages to online

E-mails from people you do not know should not be opened

Your online friends are still strangers even if you have been talking to them for a long time

"Then you need a password to keep you safe," confirmed dad.
Once the password had been set up Echo's dad moved his attention to a small symbol at the bottom corner of the screen.
"Do you know what that is?" he asked.

Echo shook his head. "No idea dad."

"It's your anti-virus protection. It stops computer viruses which can infect your programmes when you are online. A computer virus can cause lots of problems and stop your computer from working. Your password and anti-virus protection are part of your cyber security. They keep your computer safe from people who might want to access it," explained Echo's dad.

Barney smiled mysteriously and began to write something down in big red letters on a piece of paper. Echo and his friends were curious to see what it was, but Barney kept it hidden until he was finished.

Finally he held up the paper.
"Think U Know," said the eagle simply.
"Think you know what?" replied Echo blankly.
Barney laughed at the confused look on his young friends' faces.
"It's a website that tells you all about how to stay safe online."

Echo couldn't wait to type in the web address: www.thinkuknow.co.uk.

The site was full of great advice on how to stay safe when on social network sites, instant messaging, gaming and how to deal with e-mails as well as loads of other great stuff.

Echo's mum and dad allowed the friends to play on his new tablet for an hour and when they eventually logged off everyone agreed how important it was to remember some simple safety rules.

Visit **think U know**

Remember

- When you are chatting online try not to give out any personal information about yourself.

- If you receive an e-mail from someone you don't know, NEVER open it. Tell an adult you trust.

- It's not a good idea to send a picture of yourself to someone you have only met online.

- Never give your mobile phone number to someone you have not met in the real world.

- Never arrange to meet someone in person that you've only sent messages to online.

- It's a good idea to use a nickname rather than your real name.

- It's a good idea to put your real age on your site. If you lie, adults might try and contact you.

www.thinkuknow.co.uk

The following day, Spike was at home playing on her computer.

Her mum and dad were out at the shops and she had been told not to go online until they came home, but Spike couldn't wait. She had made a new friend on a site called Woodland Chat and Spike wanted to find out what her new friend was up to.

Spike logged on to the site and typed out a message.
"Hi Tipsy.....this is Spike....are you online?"

Spike loved social media and how it made keeping in touch with her friends so easy. She was always sending pictures to Dizzy, Echo and Digsby, showing her having fun and doing crazy things. She used her smart phone to take pictures and videos. It was simple and she could post them straight onto Woodland Chat or other sites. The apps on her phone even let her do it for free. Spike also liked Chat rooms where she could talk to people online. Sometimes it would be people she knew, but often it was complete strangers like Tipsy.

After a few moments, a message appeared from Tipsy.
"Hi Spike... yes I am online. How are you?"

The two hedgehogs chatted for a while about what they had been doing at school and a new boy band they both liked. Spike was enjoying chatting to Tipsy as they seemed to like so many of the same things.

Tipsy sent a new message:

"I'm online this Sunday practising my dance moves," said Tipsy, "I'd love you to watch and comment!"

"I'm supposed to be playing with my Dad and my Brother on Sunday with football afterwards," said Spike.

"Ah, please!" said Tipsy, "I really would like you to watch and tell me what you think."

"Ok," said Spike, "I'll have time to do both things, I'll log in to the Woodland Chat and watch you."

"Great!" said Tipsy, "I can't wait to see what you think!"

Web **wordsearch**

See if you can find the following words;

1) Mobile APPS are popular ways to play games.
2) When you are ONLINE in a CHATROOM do not give out your personal information.
3) Only open an E-MAIL from people you know.
4) Make sure your GAMING console has security settings.
5) The INTERNET is great fun if you are careful.
6) Your LAPTOP and TABLET should have a strong PASSWORD.
7) Only go on WEBSITES suitable for your age.
8) If you receive a nasty TEXT message tell a trusted adult.

W	S	K	A	L	I	A	M	E	U
E	W	P	F	G	H	Z	B	G	X
B	P	R	P	H	J	X	N	A	R
S	C	H	A	T	R	O	O	M	E
I	T	B	S	J	A	C	M	I	T
T	L	U	S	K	K	B	M	N	T
E	T	I	W	G	L	V	L	G	I
S	X	A	O	N	L	I	N	E	W
T	E	N	R	E	T	N	I	Z	T
P	T	S	D	P	O	T	P	A	L

On Saturday morning the friends were all back at Echo's house.

Echo's mum came into the room carrying a big tray.

"Who would like a drink and some ice cream?" she asked.

Everyone except Digsby Mole jumped up and sat at the table, spoons at the ready.

Digsby had been quiet all day. He shook his head.

"No thanks, Mrs Squirrel," he said politely. "I need to go home now."

Digsby left as the others all tucked in to the ice cream.

"What's wrong with Digsby?" asked Barney. "He looks very sad."

"I don't know," replied Echo.

"Digsby hasn't wanted to join in any games for a couple of days now. Perhaps it's because he hasn't got a computer or smart phone. His mum and dad can't afford one."

Barney wasn't convinced. He knew something was wrong with poor Digsby, and he was sure that it wasn't just because he didn't have a computer or smart phone.

"Digsby's worried about something," thought Barney. "And I need to find out what is troubling him so I can help."

As Barney the Eagle, together with Echo's dad watched Echo, Spike and Dizzy playing happily with the tablet, Barney hoped the three friends would remember the safety rules. But Barney worried that in all the excitement they might forget.
Then he had a great idea!

"Who wants to make the most new friends?" he asked.
Everyone jumped up and down shouting:

"Me, me, me..."

Barney laughed and said, "okay, meet me tomorrow morning at nine o'clock at Tom Stoat's house. We can have a competition. See you at nine o'clock, and don't forget to tell Digsby."
Barney said goodbye. He needed to see Tom Stoat the Woodland Wizard. He had a great plan, but only Tom Stoat could make it work.

Word **jumble**

Un-scramble the letters to find the correct words.

TERINTEN	....
RYBEC GULYBLIN	....
CHAK	....
XETT	....
MEALI	....
FASE	....
LONINE	....
GLOBS	....
LOPATP	....

17

The next day dawned bright with only a few fluffy white clouds breaking up the sunshine bathing Treetop Forest. Tom Stoat's house was in the middle of the tall oaks, almost completely hidden from view.

Barney was perched on a branch in the tallest of all the oaks surrounding Tom's house as he watched the animals arrive.
"Is everyone here?" called Barney from above.

Echo shook his head. "I don't know where Digsby is. I did tell him to come. Perhaps he's busy."

Barney knew that something must be wrong, but decided not to say anything just yet as he watched Spike and Dizzy giggling and whispering to each other.

"Who wants to be the first to make new friends?" asked Barney.
All three leapt into the air, shouting:
"Me, me...I want to be first."
Barney held up his wing.
"One at a time," he said calmly.
"Echo, you can be first."

Echo felt a little unsure of what was going to happen as he followed Barney through the long hallway and into Tom Stoat's special room. Once inside, Echo saw a huge computer with a screen so big it filled one complete wall of the room.

"Take a seat," said Barney. "And don't look so nervous, there is nothing to worry about."

No sooner had Echo sat down than the screen lit up with a new message.

'Hi Echo. My name is Charlie Squirrel. Can I join in your new football game and be your friend?"

Echo let out a yell of delight, "Yes of course!" he said.

The match started and Echo tried hard to play the game.

"You're really good at this game Echo," said Charlie. "How old are you?"

"I'm ten!" said Echo, "how old are you?"

"I'll be thirteen next week," said Charlie.

He sounded very grown up and Echo was excited that he'd found a new friend online who was almost a teenager.

"I'm in Mr Garry Owl's class at Treetop Forest School," said Echo.
"I bet you never do anything wrong then!" said Charlie.

"Yes I do!" said Echo trying to impress his new friend.
"Ok then prove it," said Charlie. "Meet me by the swings tomorrow and I'll bring some cider!"

"Ok then, I will!" said Echo.

He closed the laptop quickly as Barney came into Tom Stoat's special room.

"Who were you talking to?" asked Barney as he opened the tablet to a black screen.

Echo's cheeks started to turn red.

"Nobody," he lied.

Barney clicked a few buttons on the laptop and the screen came to life with a picture of a badger who was much older than Echo or any of his friends.

"Is this who you were talking to?" asked Barney

"No! It definitely wasn't that old badger!" said Echo pointing at the screen. "I made a new friend called Charlie, he's nearly thirteen and a squirrel just like me."

Barney put his arm around Echo's shoulder.

"No, that's who you thought you were talking to," said the wise old eagle. "This fully grown badger was just pretending to be your age so he could make friends with you."

"Why would he do that!" said Echo.

"I'm not sure," said Barney. "But you should remember that anyone you meet online, but never face to face in the real world, may not be who they say they are."

Echo looked shocked.

"I'll never do that again," said Echo.

Meanings 1

Join the words to the matching statements using a line.
To help you, Barney has done the first one for you.

A Blog

A Stranger

A Friend

A Hacker

A Search Engine

Internet Security

a person who you know well and who you like a lot, but who is usually not a member of your family.

is someone who might 'find' their way into your computer and access your information.

is a tool like 'Google' which helps you find information on the internet.

is a diary you can write online about yourself or your interests.

is important to protect your computer from bugs and computer viruses.

is someone you should never give details about yourself to.

Online Gaming **Safety Tips**

Only add people you know in real life, these are people you can trust

Never be mean to someone else when you're playing a game, that makes you a bully!

Language is important, don't use swear words even if others do

In App purchases can end up costing lots of money; make sure you get permission to purchase them

Nobody likes to lose, but don't get too upset if someone beats you... remember it's just a game!

Enjoying yourself is important, but don't spend too long playing games online

Gaming can be so much fun, but make sure you tell your parents when you go online

Always be careful when chatting to someone online - they may not be who they say they are!

Make sure your password is strong so no-one can hack your account

If you think you may have been tricked or cheated, don't keep it a secret. Tell someone you trust straight away

Never give anyone your personal information

Games are a great way to relax and have fun, but it's important to be careful about what you share online to keep yourself safe

True or False **Internet Safety**

When you're making an account online, you should use your real name as a username	True	False
When you're making an account online, you need a strong password that no one could guess	True	False
You should tell strangers your name when you're playing with them online	True	False
When you receive an upsetting message, you should send one back	True	False
You should never agree to meet online friends, without discussing it with your parents / guardians	True	False
Not everything that you see when you're online is accurate	True	False
Send a picture of yourself to new online friends	True	False
You should make your password easy to remember in case you forget it	True	False

It was Spike's turn in Tom Stoat's special room next.

She sat down at the computer and her favourite social media site, Woodland Chat, filled the screen.

There were lots of different animals chatting in the feed.

Spike spotted that her best online friend Tipsy had posted a video of herself dancing and Spike posted a reply with plenty of smiley faces.

Suddenly, the screen split into three.

The left-hand side of the screen showed the Woodland Chat feed that Spike was commenting on, whilst on the right hand side of the screen she could see her Dad and her brother playing in one of the best forest hedges and also some of her friends playing football in the clearing.

Her Dad and her brother, as well as all of her footballing friends stopped what they were doing and faced the screen and shouted together;

"Spike! Come and join us, we're having so much fun!"

Spike smiled and was about to get up and run outside when suddenly, Spike noticed that her online friends were posting more dance videos.

Spike instantly forgot about her Dad and her brother and the football game and she started commenting on the posts.

Barney the Eagle came into Tom Stoat's special room just as the right-hand side of the screen went black.

"All my friends are online," said Spike, "we've been sharing dance tips!"

"What about your Dad and your brother?," asked Barney, "or your friends playing football?"

"I can see them anytime!" laughed Spike.

Barney put his arm around Spike's shoulder.

"Do you think by spending so much time on Woodland Chat that you might be missing other things that are happening?" asked Barney.

"But there's always something interesting happening online!" said Spike.

"Why not do both?" said Barney. "If you set yourself a limit on how much time you spend online, you could still chat with your online friends and do other things with your family and friends too."

"How do I do that?" asked Spike.

"You can set an alarm to sound if you are online for a certain amount of time," said Barney.

"That's good!" said Spike.

"How long do you think you should spend online at any one time?" asked Barney.

Spike thought for a few moments.

"One hour?" she said at last.

Barney clicked a few buttons and showed Spike how to set an alarm for one hour.

"There you go," said Barney. "Now you'll know when your online time has ended, and you can shut down and go out to play with your friends or spend time with your family."

"Thank you Barney!" said Spike. "You're the best!"

Secret Message

Fill in the missing letters to reveal the words.

1. Always tell your P _ _ _ N _ S when
   you go O _ L I _ E
2. When you are online never give anyone
   your P E _ S O _ _ L information
3. Be careful if someone asks you to keep
   something S _ C _ E _
4. Don't send P _ C T _ _ E S of yourself
   to people you don't know
5. A _ U _ TS who wish to harm you may
   pretend they are C _ _ L D _ _ N
6. The I _ T E _ N _ T can be great fun if
   you are C _ R E F _ _
7. Don't open an E _ A _ L from someone
   you don't know.
8. Try and make P A _ _ W O _ D S hard to guess
9. Don't talk to S _ R _ N G _ R _ online
10. Make sure you have security S _ T T _ N G _
    on your G _ _ _ S console

Help Spike
stay safe on the web

Spike has a new laptop computer. Before she starts using it, Spike needs to set up a P******d and make sure A*** V***s has been added.

Spike loves to chat and she likes Chat Rooms. Spike should talk to her parents/guardians about which Chat Rooms are safe to use and what she should say in them. Yes ☐   No ☐

If you don't protect your computer with anti-virus and passwords what could happen?

Cybersecurity is very important to protect your computer. Yes ☐ No ☐ Following the rules of ThinkUKnow is very important to protect yourself online. Yes ☐   No ☐

Sometimes, Spike posts pictures of herself and her friends having fun. Is it only her friends who can see the pictures or is it possible strangers might see them as well?

It can be fun to tease friends or people you know online with texts or photos. Dizzy thought he was teasing his friend Digsby, but Digsby was hurt and upset. When that happens teasing becomes B*****g.

Meanings 2

Join the words to the matching statements using a line.
To help you, Barney has done the first one for you.

Social Media   mobile computer

                    Daniell   short for applications - these
Tablet   are shortcuts to computer
                                    programmes, often used for
                                    games and social media

Post   computer software used to
                                    prevent, detect and remove
                                    malicious software

Apps   to add content to social
                                    media

Identity Theft   create and share content
                                    and/or participate in
                                    social networking

Anti-virus Protection

                                    where a person takes your
                                    private information and
                                    pretends to be you online

Dizzy was really curious now. He had seen his friends come out of the special room and they had both told him that it had been quite an experience. Barney had asked Spike and Echo not to spoil the surprise for Dizzy and both had kept their promise!

Dizzy couldn't wait for his turn.

Barney closed the door and asked Dizzy to sit down at the table. Once again the wall was filled with a huge picture, this time showing a mobile phone with the text message:

"Ha Ha...Digsby smells of soil...Digsby wears big glasses...Digsby hasn't got a smart phone..."

Dizzy looked shocked and turned to Barney who had a very stern look on his face.

"Do you recognise those words?" Barney asked.

Dizzy nodded. "It's what Spike and I have been texting to Digsby. It was only meant to be a bit of fun though. We didn't mean any harm."

Again, the words disappeared and a picture came onto the screen. This time it showed the forest full of police officers searching for something. They were pulling back bushes and looking in all the holes. Dizzy wondered what they were looking for.

Digsby's mum and dad came into view. Digsby's dad had his arm around his wife who was crying.

Dizzy looked across at Barney. "They are looking for Digsby aren't they?" he asked.

Dizzy began to cry.

"Please tell me Digsby is alright. We were only teasing him." The screen went completely blank and then disappeared into the wall. Dizzy's question was not going to be answered.

"You might have thought that sending spiteful texts was fun," said Barney. "But how did they make Digsby feel? You know how upset he has been lately. What you thought of as harmless teasing has got another name: cyber bullying!"

Dizzy felt so ashamed. He and Spike were cyber bullies. They hadn't really thought about the consequences of sending the text messages. Poor Digsby didn't know who they were from and they had made him very scared and upset.

Dizzy jumped up from the chair.

"I have to tell Spike how silly we have been," he said.
"We have to find Digsby and tell him how sorry we are for being so stupid. I hope that he will still be our friend."

Barney opened the door and let Dizzy out of the special room.

"Friendship is very important," said Barney. "It doesn't matter how many friends you have, it's how you treat them and how they treat you that is important."

Mobile phone safety tips:

Keep your phone with you
If you're worried about someone taking it,
keep it hidden from sight

Be careful with your number
Only give it to your friends and people that you trust
Don't lend your phone to someone you don't know
Or put it in a place where other people could get hold of it

Use a PIN
Most phones allow you to lock your phone with a PIN code.
If you don't have the code you can't
unlock it, so if anyone steals your
phone they won't be able to use it

**Don't be pressured to give
your number out**
If someone is pressuring you into
giving them your number, tell someone
about it such as a teacher or a parent

Switch your Bluetooth off
If you have Bluetooth on your phone,
keep it switched off when you are not using it

Meanings 3

Join the words to the matching statements using a line.
To help you, Barney has done the first one for you.

Passwords

are places where people can chat online and send pictures

Chatrooms

is a way of sending messages and letters over the internet

Instant Messaging

is when someone sends hurtful or nasty messages by text or online

E-Mail

is a mobile phone that has many of the abilities that a computer has. It may have a touchscreen, internet, and be able to run downloaded apps

Smartphone

help keep you safe and should only be shared with parents

Cyber Bullying

lets you 'talk' to anyone or your contact list as long as that person is online. You type messages to each other into a small window that shows up on both of your screens

It was a new day in Treetop Forest as Barney glided over the sparkling river far below. From up here he could see Echo at home in the big elm tree and the rest of the gang down by the river.

Echo was sitting on a branch taking in the morning sun and getting ready to go out and play after spending an hour on his tablet. His mum and dad had agreed to let him use the tablet for a couple of hours a day, provided that he remembered how to stay safe, especially when online.

Spike was waiting to meet her new friend, Tipsy.
Spike had asked her mum and dad to go with her to meet Tipsy in person, and when Tipsy arrived, she was with her mum and dad too.
The girls were really pleased to meet each other and enjoyed chatting while the adults went for a walk around a castle.
The two hedgehogs were to become great friends.

As he dipped his wings and soared off over Treetop Forest, Barney was happy to know that all his friends were safe.

Over by the Old Mill, Spike, Tipsy and Dizzy were splashing in the shallow pools with Digsby. Spike had introduced Tipsy to her friends and they all played well together.

Barney was happy to see Digsby smiling again.
All the bullying texts had stopped and he had forgiven his two friends. It was time to buy a computer for a certain young mole who had had a bit of a sad time lately and Barney felt sure that this mole would definitely follow the rules for staying safe online.

A message from
Barney & Echo

You can have lots of fun and find out interesting and useful information by going online.

But remember - follow the simple safety rules and keep safe!

Remember Internet Safety

I nform your parents when you are going online

N ever open e-mails from people you do not know

T ell a trusted adult if someone asks you to meet them

E verything you add to a social networking site can be copied or printed

R emember to change your password regularly

N umbers in passwords make them harder to guess

E njoy the internet, it can be great fun

T alk to a trusted adult if you are upset or worried

S ending pictures to people you don't know is not a good idea

A sk your parents before downloading apps

F ollowing some simple rules will help you stay safe online

E xcessive use of the internet can be harmful

T elling strangers details about yourself is not a good idea

Y ou can stay safe and still have fun online

Don't forget to bring the book back into school!

Parent Activity

Internet Safety True or False

Answer the true or false questions below, then take this book home and ask your parents or guardians to help by answering the questions too...

Circle the correct answer.

	Your answer	Parents answer
1. Having a strong password is really important	True False	True False
2. If you meet someone online it is ok to give them your address and phone number	True False	True False
3. Someone you meet online has asked you to send your picture. You should say no	True False	True False
4. If you receive an e-mail asking for your password you should not reply	True False	True False
5. Passwords with a mix of letters and numbers are more secure	True False	True False
6. There is no need to have up to date anti-virus software on your computer	True False	True False
7. It is up to the internet provider to make sure you are safe online	True False	True False
8. Some people who you meet online may not be who they say they are	True False	True False
9. Setting parental controls helps keep you safer online	True False	True False

Don't forget to bring the book back into school!

Remember Cyber Bullying

Cyber Bullying is when people send nasty and upsetting messages

You should always tell a trusted adult if you receive nasty messages

Bullying is never a nice thing to do to others

Every time you get a nasty message make a note of it and tell a trusted adult

Replying to nasty messages is not a good idea

Be careful who you give your mobile phone number to

Upsetting messages should always be reported

Learn the 'Think u Know' Cyber Bullying safety rules

Let a trusted adult know if you think one of your friends is being bullied

You can get lots of help if you are being bullied

It is not your fault if you are bullied

Nasty messages may seem like just a bit of fun but they are not

Good friends will always help you

Don't forget to bring the book back into school!

Cyber Bullying True or False

Answer the true or false questions below, then take this book home and ask your parents or guardians to help by answering the questions too...

Circle the correct answer.	Your answer	Parents answer
1. If I am upset about being bullied I should keep this secret	True False	True False
2. All nasty messages and e-mails should be kept and shown to a trusted adult	True False	True False
3. Bullying is a normal part of growing up and should be ignored	True False	True False
4. If you receive a nasty message you should send a nasty message back	True False	True False
5. Anyone can become a victim of Cyber Bullying	True False	True False
6. You cannot spot a bully just by the way they act or post comments	True False	True False
7. Cyber Bullying affects people of any age and from any background	True False	True False
8. Many children will not speak to an adult if they are bullied as they feel ashamed	True False	True False

Don't forget to bring the book back into school!

Barney Says...

if you feel as though you are being bullied online
or you see anyone being bullied don't just sit back
and watch, tell someone!

The best idea is to tell your parent, guardian or your teacher the very
first time it happens – or at least as quickly as possible.

The best way to deal with a bully is to - REPORT THEM and then IGNORE THEM!

Block the bully from all of your social media
platforms. Block them on your mobile phone
and then make sure you take them off your
gaming console player list.

Don't retaliate in any way that's angry,
offensive or threatening – you might feel
sad, alone or even afraid, but if you tell your
parent, guardian or teacher what's happening
straight away you'll feel better.
www.internetmatters.org has some great advice.

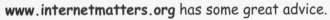

Barney Says…don't become a cyberbully yourself!

Never post anything offensive or rude about anyone, even if they are your friend and you're only joking. Don't swear at your friends or other people on your gaming console or in an online post or comment and never repost or send on anything with a swear word in it.

If you see any posts that are rude or hurtful report them through the social media site that you saw them on, or by visiting **www.thinkyouknow.co.uk** and using the online tools

REMEMBER: IF YOU SEE BULLYING ONLINE, DON'T JUST SIT BACK AND WATCH – **TELL SOMEONE!**

The UK Council for Child Internet Safety

New technologies inspire children to be creative, communicate and learn. However, while the internet is a great resource, it is important that children and young people are protected from the risks they may encounter. The UK Council for Child Internet Safety (UKCCIS) is a group of more than 200 organisations drawn from across government, industry, law, academia and charity sectors that work in partnership to help keep children safe online.

UKCCIS achievements include the creation of:
*   a family friendly internet and a code of practice drawn up by service providers following a consultation about parental internet controls;
*   advice for industry providers on effective internet safety messages they should use;
*   advice for industry providers on social networking, moderation, search and chat;
*   and summaries of a large body of internet safety research.

Why do we need a UK Council for Child Internet Safety?

The internet is a vital part of British life, and our dependence on it will only increase as today's children and young people become adults. In 2013, 91% of all 5-15 year olds used the internet. The estimated weekly volume of internet use at home in the same year increased with the age of the child: 6 hours for 5-7 year olds, 8.1 hours for 8-11 year olds and 17.1 hours for 12-15 year olds. (source: Ofcom)

In the UK, 48% of children say there are things on the internet that bother children their own age and 13% of 9-16 year olds say that they've been bothered/upset by something online (according to EU Kids Online). Around 10% of 8-15 year olds who use the internet at home report seeing things that make them feel sad, frightened or embarrassed online (source: Ofcom).

The internet provides children and young people with a wealth of opportunities for their entertainment, communication and education. But there are also risks of harm through the deliberate behaviour of others online and through exposure to inappropriate content. As a result, if today's children are going to play their full part as digital citizens they need to be able to deal with the risks.